# 100 GRADED FLUTE SOLOS

# 100
# GRADED
# FLUTE
# SOLOS

**WISE PUBLICATIONS**
*part of The Music Sales Group*

London / New York / Paris / Sydney / Copenhagen / Berlin / Madrid / Tokyo

Published by
**Wise Publications**
14-15 Berners Street, London W1T 3LJ, UK.

Exclusive Distributors:
**Music Sales Limited**
Distribution Centre, Newmarket Road,
Bury St Edmunds, Suffolk IP33 3YB, UK.
**Music Sales Pty Limited**
120 Rothschild Avenue, Rosebery, NSW 2018, Australia.

Order No. AM988350
ISBN 13: 978-1-84609-835-2
ISBN 10: 1-84609-835-1
This book © Copyright 2007 Wise Publications,
a division of Music Sales Limited.

Edited by Jessica Williams.
Music processed by Paul Ewers Music Design.
Cover design by Michael Bell Design.
Printed in the EU.

**Your Guarantee of Quality**
As publishers, we strive to produce every book to
the highest commercial standards.
This book has been carefully designed to minimise awkward
page turns and to make playing from it a real pleasure.
Particular care has been given to specifying acid-free, neutral-sized
paper made from pulps which have not been elemental chlorine bleached.
This pulp is from farmed sustainable forests and
was produced with special regard for the environment.
Throughout, the printing and binding have been planned to ensure
a sturdy, attractive publication which should give years of enjoyment.
If your copy fails to meet our high standards,
please inform us and we will gladly replace it.

**www.musicsales.com**

# GRADING NOTES

The pieces in this book have been carefully graded according to
various criteria such as rhythmic complexity, phrasing, tempo, key, range, etc.
Look for the number of stars for each piece to give you
an idea of the approximate playing level.
All musicians have particular strengths and weaknesses,
so the grading offered here should be taken as a suggestion only.

Generally, pieces with one star have simple rhythms,
straight forward phrasings and few difficult intervals;
essentially diatonic and in easier keys.

Pieces with two stars will have more challenging passages,
perhaps containing more rhythmic complexity,
more advanced key signatures and possibly long-held notes
requiring an increased strength of embouchure.

Three-star pieces may include chromaticism,
challenging articulation and more advanced fingerings.
Read through rhythms and keys before playing, and check for
time-signature changes and correct phrasing.

# Angels

Words & Music by Robbie Williams & Guy Chambers

8

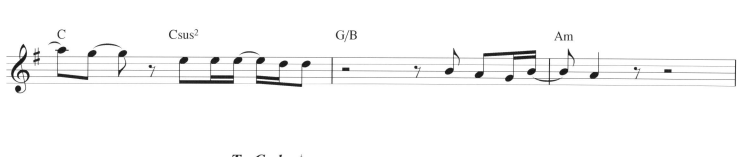

*To Coda* ⊕

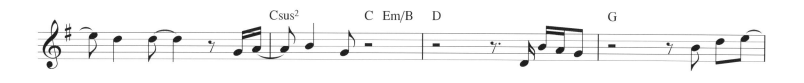

*D.S. al Coda*

⊕ *Coda*

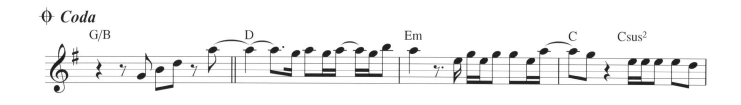

# Angie

Words & Music by Mick Jagger & Keith Richards

# Beautiful

Words & Music by Linda Perry

# ...Baby One More Time

Words & Music by Max Martin

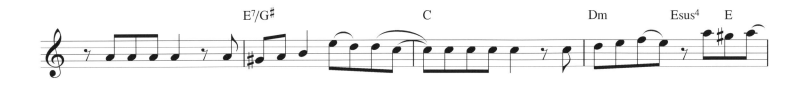

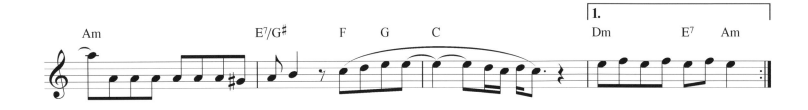

12

# Beautiful Stranger

Words & Music by Madonna & William Orbit

# The Best

Words & Music by Mike Chapman & Holly Knight

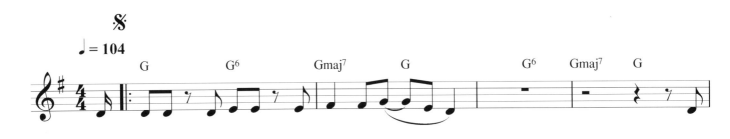

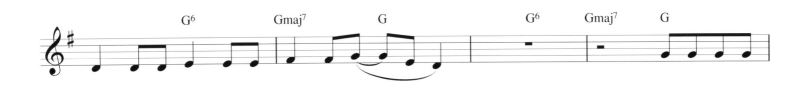

Coda

# Big Spender

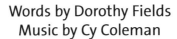

Words by Dorothy Fields
Music by Cy Coleman

**Moderate Swing**

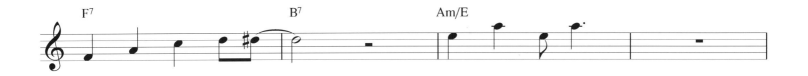

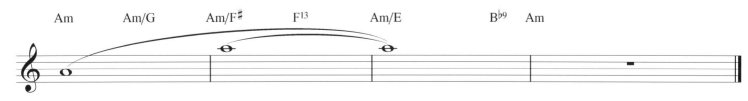

# Born Free

Words by Don Black
Music by John Barry

# Born To Try

Words & Music by Delta Goodrem & Audius Mtawarira

# Bridge Over Troubled Water

Words & Music by Paul Simon

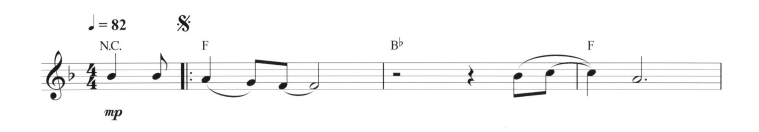

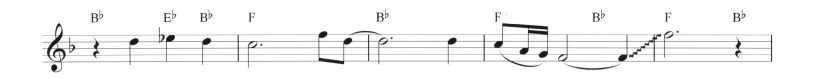

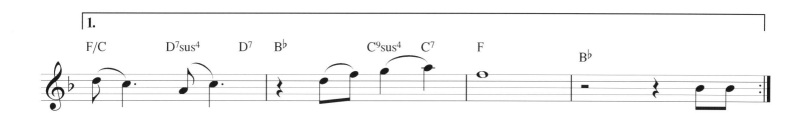

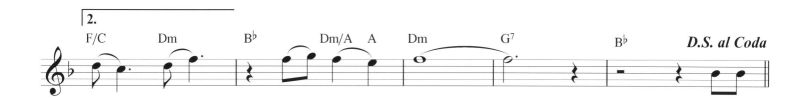

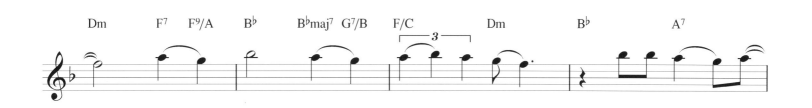

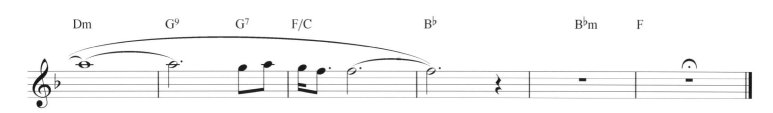

# Can You Feel The Love Tonight
## (from 'The Lion King')

Words by Tim Rice
Music by Elton John

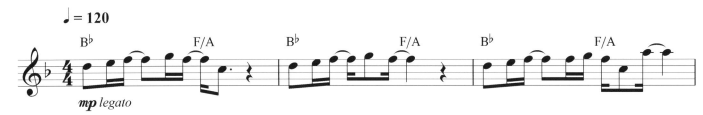

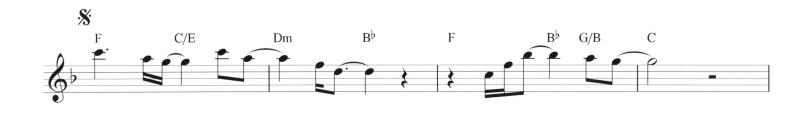

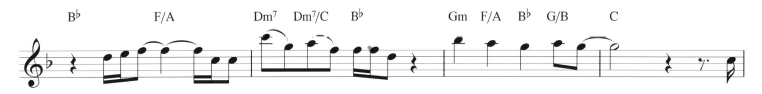

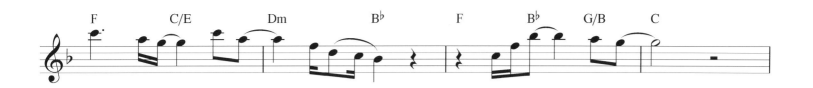

*To Coda* ⊕

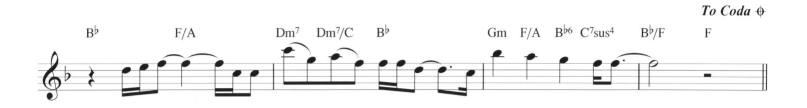

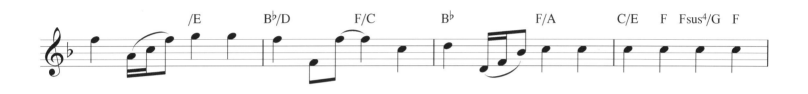

*D.S. al Coda*

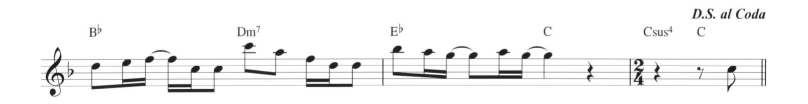

⊕ *Coda*

# Brown Eyed Girl

Words & Music by Van Morrison

# Can't Get You Out Of My Head

Words & Music by Cathy Dennis & Rob Davis

# Can't Help Falling In Love

Words & Music by George David Weiss, Hugo Peretti & Luigi Creatore

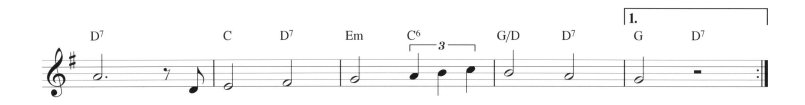

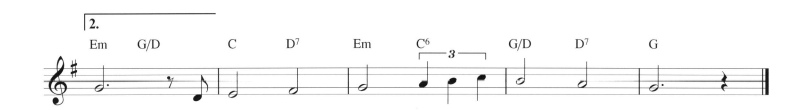

# Clocks

Words & Music by Guy Berryman, Chris Martin, Jon Buckland & Will Champion

# Crazy

Words & Music by Thomas Callaway, Brian Burton, Gianfranco Reverberi & Gian Piero Reverberi

# Cry Me A River

*Words & Music by Justin Timberlake, Scott Storch & Tim Mosley*

# Don't Cry For Me Argentina
## (from 'Evita')

Music by Andrew Lloyd Webber
Lyrics by Tim Rice

# Don't Get Around Much Anymore

Words by Bob Russell
Music by Duke Ellington

# Don't Know Why

Words & Music by Jesse Harris

# Don't Look Back In Anger

Words & Music by Noel Gallagher

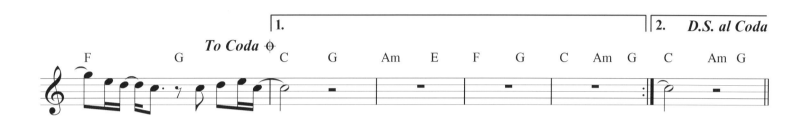

# The Entertainer

Music by Scott Joplin

# (Everything I Do) I Do It For You

Words by Bryan Adams & Robert John Lange
Music by Michael Kamen

# Fairytale Of New York

Words & Music by Shane MacGowan & Jem Finer

# Feeling Good

Words & Music by Leslie Bricusse & Anthony Newley

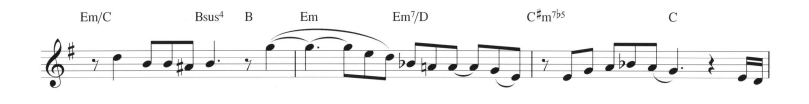

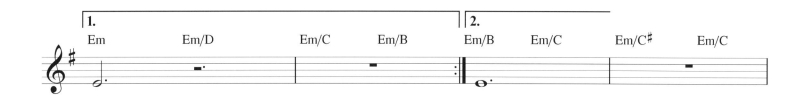

Em   Em/D   Em/C   Em/B

𝄋 *Coda*

A⁷                    F#                    D

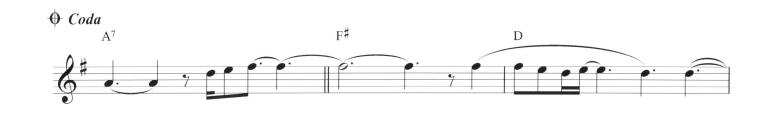

C⁷                    B⁷          N.C.      Em        Em/D

Em/C          Em/B          Em          Em/D          Em/C          Em/B

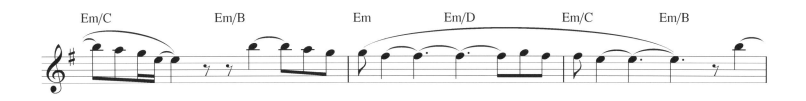

Em      Em⁷/D              C#m⁷♭⁵          C          Em/B          Em/A

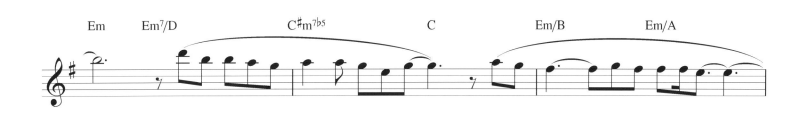

G          F#⁷sus⁴  B/F#    A⁷          B⁷                    Em

# Fever

Words & Music by John Davenport & Eddie Cooley

**Moderate jump beat**

# Fields Of Gold

Words & Music by Sting

# Fly Me To The Moon
## (In Other Words)

Words & Music by Bart Howard

# Fix You

Words & Music by Guy Berryman, Chris Martin, Jon Buckland & Will Champion

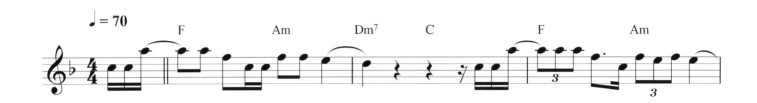

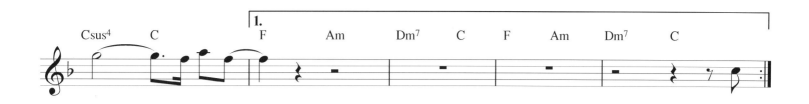

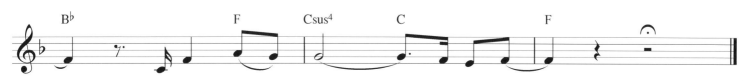

# Girl, You'll Be A Woman Soon

Words & Music by Neil Diamond

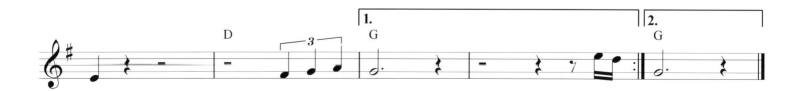

# The Godfather (Love Theme)

Music by Nino Rota

# Gold

Words & Music by Prince

# Goldfinger

Words by Leslie Bricusse & Anthony Newley
Music by John Barry

# Golden Touch

Words & Music by Johnny Borrell

54

# Gravity

Words & Music by Guy Berryman, Chris Martin, Jon Buckland & Will Champion

# Hero

Words & Music by Enrique Iglesias, Paul Barry & Mark Taylor

# Hallelujah

Words & Music by Leonard Cohen

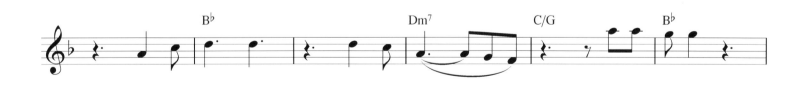

# Heaven

Words & Music by Bryan Adams & Jim Vallance

# Hey Jude

Words & Music by John Lennon & Paul McCartney

# I Get The Sweetest Feeling

Words & Music by Van McCoy & Alicia Evelyn

# I Got You (I Feel Good)

Words & Music by James Brown

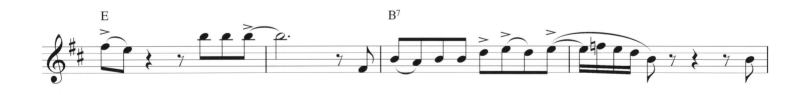

# I Will Always Love You

Words & Music by Dolly Parton

# Imagine

Words & Music by John Lennon

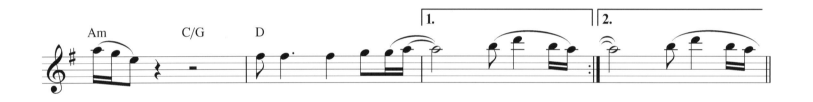

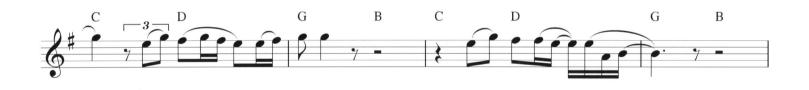

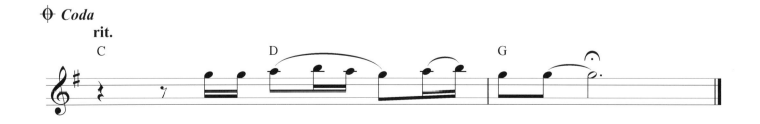

# Is It Any Wonder?

Words & Music by Richard Hughes, James Sanger, Tim Rice-Oxley & Tom Chaplin

# Ironic

**Words by Alanis Morissette**
**Music by Alanis Morissette & Glen Ballard**

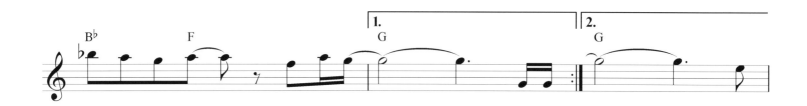

**_D.S. al Coda_**

**Coda**

# Israelites

Words & Music by Desmond Dacres & Leslie Kong

# Knockin' On Heaven's Door

Words & Music by Bob Dylan

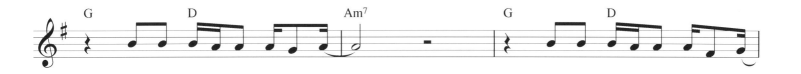

# It's Not Unusual

Words & Music by Gordon Mills & Les Reed

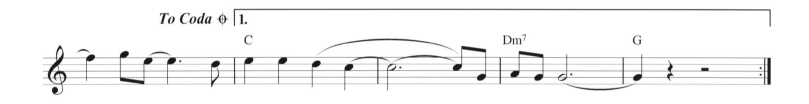

**D.C. al Coda**

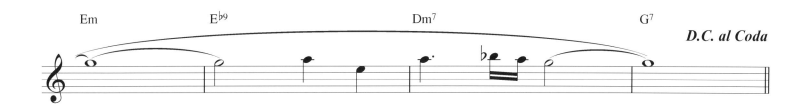

**Coda**

*Fade to end*

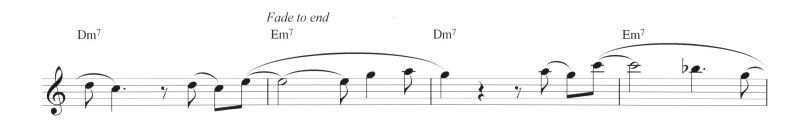

# Just The Way I'm Feeling

Words & Music by Grant Nicholas

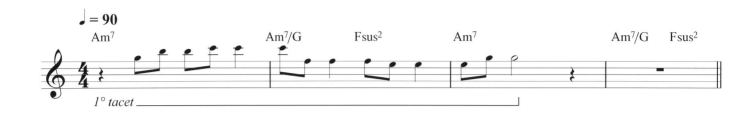

# The Lady In Red

Words & Music by Chris de Burgh

# Leave Right Now

Words & Music by Francis White

# Let It Be

Words & Music by John Lennon & Paul McCartney

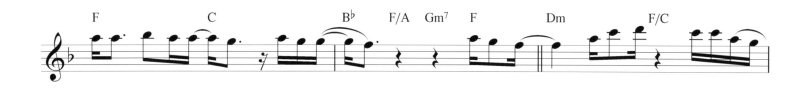

80

⊕ *Coda*

*rall.*

# Like A Virgin

Words & Music by Billy Steinberg & Tom Kelly

# Lover Man
## (Oh Where Can You Be)

Words & Music by Jimmy Davis, Roger Ramirez & Jimmy Sherman

**Slow Blues**

# Livin' On A Prayer

Words & Music by Richie Sambora, Desmond Child & Jon Bon Jovi

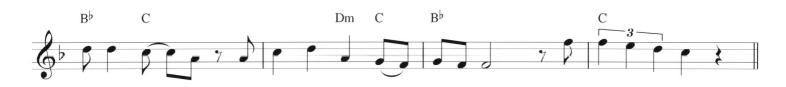

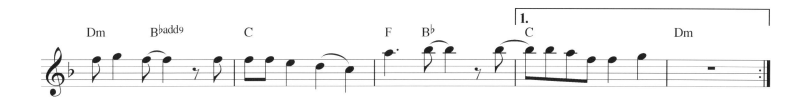

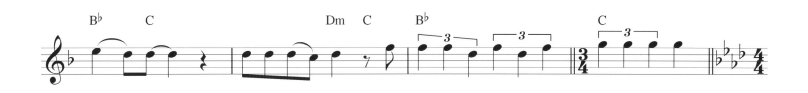

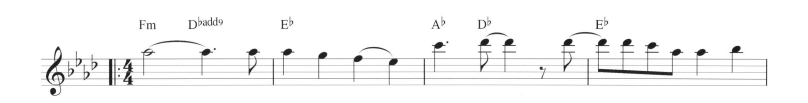

# Lovin' You

Words & Music by Minnie Riperton & Richard Rudolph

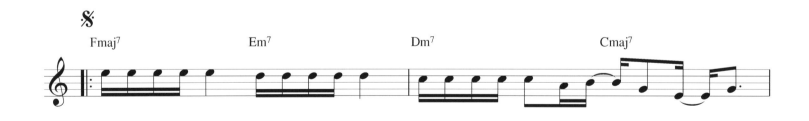

***D.S. al Coda***

𝄌 ***Coda***

# Memory
## (from 'Cats')

Music by Andrew Lloyd Webber
Text by Trevor Nunn after T.S. Eliot

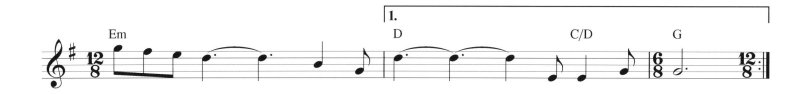

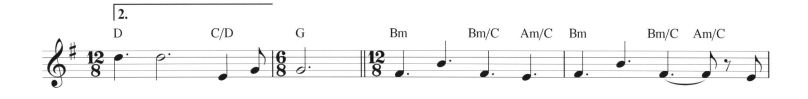

# Mad World

Words & Music by Roland Orzabal

# Missing

**Words by Tracey Thorn**
**Music by Ben Watt**

# Mission: Impossible

Music by Lalo Schifrin

92

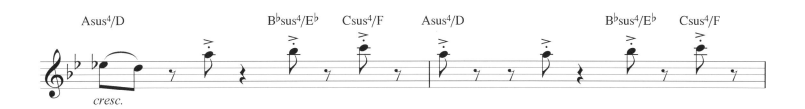

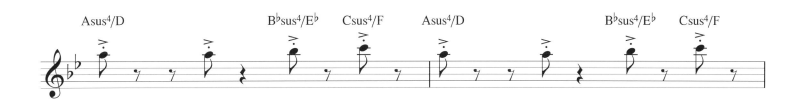

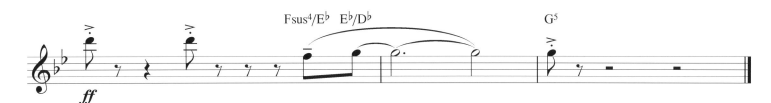

# The Model

Words & Music by Ralf Hutter, Karl Bartos & Emil Schult

# Moon River

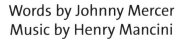

Words by Johnny Mercer
Music by Henry Mancini

# Mrs. Robinson

Words & Music by Paul Simon

# Nothing In My Way

Words & Music by Richard Hughes, James Sanger, Tim Rice-Oxley & Tom Chaplin

# Oh Yeah (On The Radio)

Words & Music by Bryan Ferry

# One

Words & Music by David Evans, Adam Clayton, Paul Hewson & Laurence Mullen

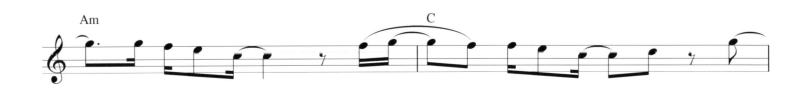

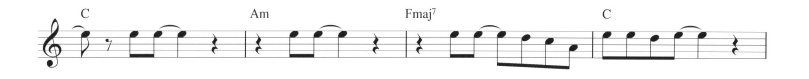

# Other Side Of The World

Words & Music by KT Tunstall & Martin Terefe

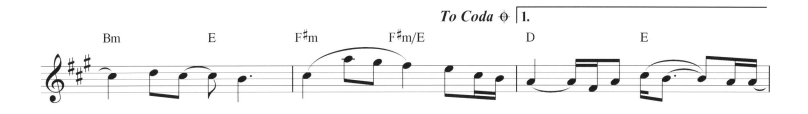

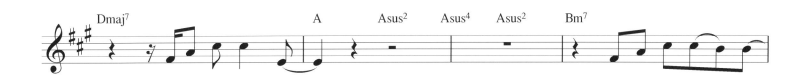

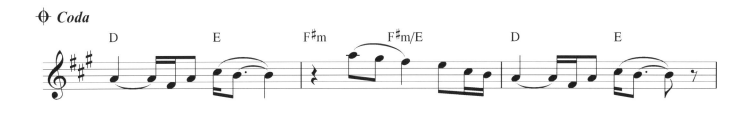

# Orange Coloured Sky

Words & Music by Milton DeLugg & Willie Stein

# Penny Lane

*Words & Music by John Lennon & Paul McCartney*

# Perfect

Words & Music by Mark E. Nevin

# The Power Of Love

Words & Music by Holly Johnson, Mark O'Toole, Peter Gill & Brian Nash

# Put Your Records On

Words & Music by John Beck, Steven Chrisanthou & Corinne Bailey Rae

# Sail Away

Words & Music by David Gray

# Run

Words & Music by Gary Lightbody, Jonathan Quinn, Mark McClelland, Nathan Connolly & Iain Archer

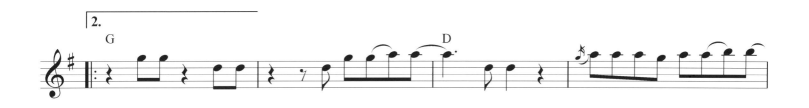

111

# She Moves In Her Own Way

Words & Music by Luke Pritchard, Hugh Harris, Max Rafferty & Paul Garred

# She's Not There

Words & Music by Rod Argent

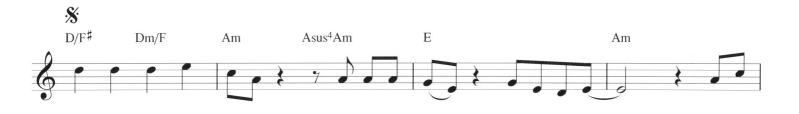

# She's The One

Words & Music by Karl Wallinger

# Somebody Told Me

Words & Music by Brandon Flowers, Dave Keuning, Mark Stoermer & Ronnie Van Nucci

116

# Son Of A Preacher Man

Words & Music by John Hurley & Ronnie Wilkins

118

# (Sittin' On) The Dock Of The Bay

Words & Music by Steve Cropper & Otis Redding

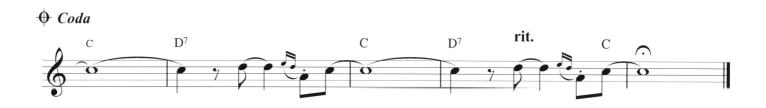

# Stand By Me

Words & Music by Ben E. King, Jerry Leiber & Mike Stoller

# Strangers In The Night

Words by Charles Singleton & Eddie Snyder
Music by Bert Kaempfert

# Sweet Caroline

Words & Music by Neil Diamond

# 'Tain't What You Do
## (It's The Way That Cha Do It)

Words & Music by Sy Oliver & James Young

# Tainted Love

Words & Music by Ed Cobb

# Take Me To The River

Words & Music by Al Green & Mabon Hodges

# Tears In Heaven

Words & Music by Eric Clapton & Will Jennings

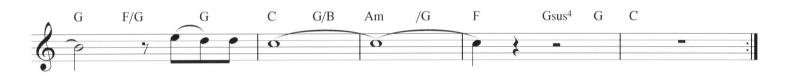

# The Song From Moulin Rouge
## (Where Is Your Heart)

Words by William Engvick
Music by Georges Auric

# True Faith

*Words & Music by Peter Hook, Stephen Hague, Bernard Sumner, Gillian Gilbert & Stephen Morris*

# Unchained Melody

Words by Hy Zaret
Music by Alex North

# Video Killed The Radio Star

Words & Music by Geoffrey Downes, Trevor Horn & Bruce Woolley

# Waterloo

Words & Music by Benny Andersson, Stig Anderson & Björn Ulvaeus

# The Way You Look Tonight

Words by Dorothy Fields
Music by Jerome Kern

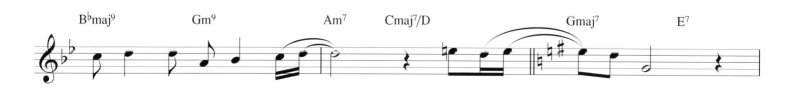

### Coda

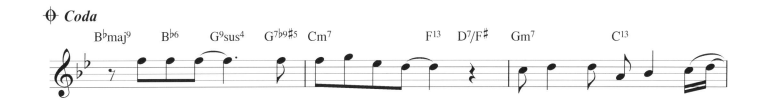

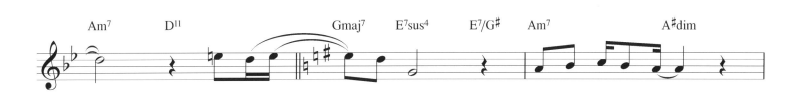

rit.

# What A Wonderful World

Words & Music by George Weiss & Bob Thiele

# Yellow

Words & Music by Guy Berryman, Jon Buckland, Will Champion & Chris Martin

# Wonderwall

Words & Music by Noel Gallagher

# Yesterday

Words & Music by John Lennon & Paul McCartney

Medium ballad ♩ = 98

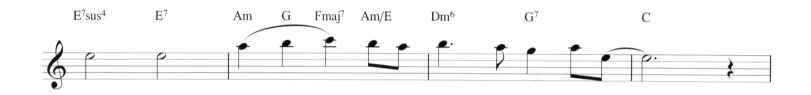

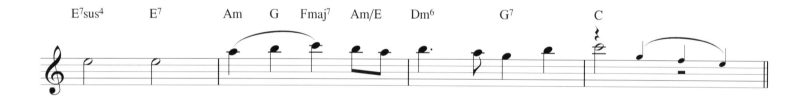

140

# Your Song

Words & Music by Elton John & Bernie Taupin

# You're Beautiful

Words & Music by Sacha Skarbek, James Blunt & Amanda Ghost

**To Coda I** ⊕

**D.S. al Coda I**

⊕ **Coda I**

**D.S. al Coda II**

⊕ **Coda II**

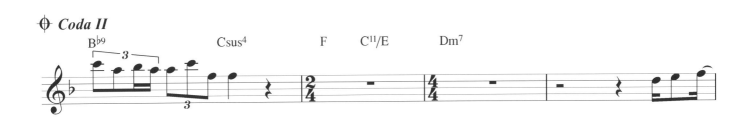

# You're The One That I Want

*Words & Music by John Farrar*